My Book of Songs and Lullabies

Kali Stileman

PICTURE CORGI

My Book of Songs and Lullabies

If You're Happy and You Know It

If you're happy and you know it, clap your hands.
If you're happy and you know it, clap your hands.
If you're happy and you know it,
And you really want to show it,
If you're happy and you know it, clap your hands.

If you're happy and you know it, nod your head.
If you're happy and you know it, nod your head.
If you're happy and you know it,
And you really want to show it,
If you're happy and you know it, nod your head.

If you're happy and you know it, stamp your feet.
If you're happy and you know it, stamp your feet.
If you're happy and you know it,
And you really want to show it,
If you're happy and you know it, stamp your feet.

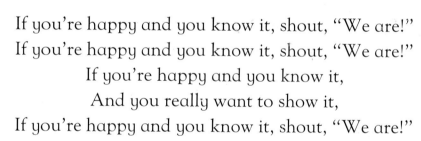

If you're happy and you know it, shout, "We are!"
If you're happy and you know it, shout, "We are!"
If you're happy and you know it,
And you really want to show it,
If you're happy and you know it, shout, "We are!"

There Was an Old Lady

There was an old lady who swallowed a fly,
I don't know why she swallowed a fly – perhaps she'll die!

There was an old lady who swallowed a spider,
That wriggled and wiggled and jiggled inside her;
She swallowed the spider to catch the fly;
I don't know why she swallowed a fly – perhaps she'll die!

There was an old lady who swallowed a bird;
How absurd to swallow a bird!
She swallowed the bird to catch the spider,
She swallowed the spider to catch the fly;
I don't know why she swallowed a fly – perhaps she'll die!

There was an old lady who swallowed a cat;
Fancy that to swallow a cat!
She swallowed the cat to catch the bird,
She swallowed the bird to catch the spider,
She swallowed the spider to catch the fly;
I don't know why she swallowed a fly – perhaps she'll die!

There was an old lady that swallowed a dog;
What a hog, to swallow a dog!
She swallowed the dog to catch the cat,
She swallowed the cat to catch the bird,
She swallowed the bird to catch the spider,
She swallowed the spider to catch the fly;
I don't know why she swallowed a fly – perhaps she'll die!

There was an old lady that swallowed a cow;
I don't know how she swallowed a cow!
She swallowed the cow to catch the dog,
She swallowed the dog to catch the cat,
She swallowed the cat to catch the bird,
She swallowed the bird to catch the spider,
She swallowed the spider to catch the fly;
I don't know why she swallowed a fly – perhaps she'll die!

There was an old lady who swallowed a horse...
She's dead, of course!

This Old Man

This old man, he played one,
He played nick nack on my thumb;
With a nick nack, paddy whack,
Give a dog a bone,
This old man came rolling home.

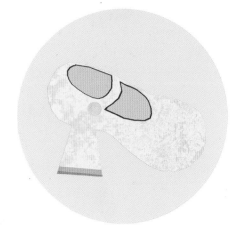

This old man, he played two,
He played nick nack on my shoe;
With a nick nack, paddy whack,
Give a dog a bone,
This old man came rolling home.

This old man, he played three,
He played nick nack on my knee;
With a nick nack, paddy whack,
Give a dog a bone,
This old man came rolling home.

This old man, he played four,
He played nick nack on my door;
With a nick nack, paddy whack,
Give a dog a bone,
This old man came rolling home.

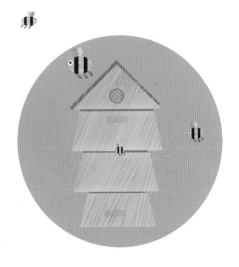

This old man, he played five,
He played nick nack on my hive;
With a nick nack, paddy whack,
Give a dog a bone,
This old man came rolling home.

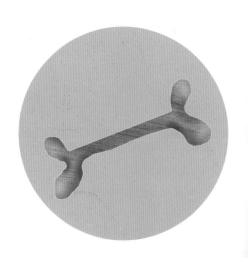

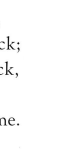

This old man, he played six,
He played nick nack with a stick;
With a nick nack, paddy whack,
Give a dog a bone,
This old man came rolling home.

This old man, he played seven,
He played nick nack up in heaven;
With a nick nack, paddy whack,
Give a dog a bone,
This old man came rolling home.

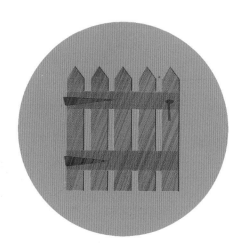

This old man, he played eight,
He played nick nack on my gate;
With a nick nack, paddy whack,
Give a dog a bone,
This old man came rolling home.

This old man, he played nine,
He played nick nack on my spine;
With a nick nack, paddy whack,
Give a dog a bone,
This old man came rolling home.

This old man, he played ten,
He played nick nack once again;
With a nick nack, paddy whack,
Give a dog a bone,
This old man came rolling home.

The Wheels on the Bus

The wheels on the bus go round and round,
Round and round,
Round and round.
The wheels on the bus go round and round,
All through the town.

The wipers on the bus go swish, swish, swish,
Swish, swish, swish,
Swish, swish, swish.
The wipers on the bus go swish, swish, swish,
All through the town.

The horn on the bus goes beep, beep, beep,
Beep, beep, beep,
Beep, beep, beep.
The horn on the bus goes beep, beep, beep,
All through the town.

Oranges and Lemons

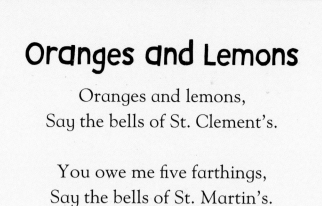

Oranges and lemons,
Say the bells of St. Clement's.

You owe me five farthings,
Say the bells of St. Martin's.

When will you pay me?
Say the bells of Old Bailey.

When I grow rich,
Say the bells of Shoreditch.

When will that be?
Say the bells of Stepney.

I do not know,
Says the great bell of Bow.

Here comes a candle
To light you to bed,

And here comes a chopper
To chop off your head!

Row Your Boat

Row, row, row your boat,
Gently down the stream.
Merrily, merrily, merrily, merrily,
Life is but a dream.

Rub-a-Dub-Dub

Rub-a-dub-dub,
Three men in a tub,
And how do you think they got there?
The butcher, the baker,
The candlestick-maker,
They all jumped out of a baked potato,
'Twas enough to make a man stare.

Here We Go Round the Mulberry Bush

Here we go round the mulberry bush,
The mulberry bush, the mulberry bush.
Here we go round the mulberry bush,
On a cold and frosty morning.

This is the way we wash our clothes,
Wash our clothes, wash our clothes.
This is the way we wash our clothes,
On a cold and frosty morning.

This is the way we clap our hands,
Clap our hands, clap our hands.
This is the way we clap our hands,
On a cold and frosty morning.

Ring-a-Ring o'Roses

Ring-a-ring-o'roses,
A pocket full of posies,
A-tishoo, a-tishoo!
We all fall down.

I Had a Little Nut Tree

I had a little nut tree,
Nothing would it bear
But a silver nutmeg,
And a golden pear.
The King of Spain's daughter
Came to visit me,
And all for the sake
Of my little nut tree.

Her dress was made of crimson,
Jet black was her hair,
She asked me for my nut tree
And my golden pear.
I said, "So fair a princess
Never did I see,
I'll give you all the fruit
From my little nut tree."

London Bridge

London Bridge is falling down,
Falling down, falling down.
London Bridge is falling down,
My fair lady.

Build it up with wood and clay,
Wood and clay, wood and clay.
Build it up with wood and clay,
My fair lady.

Wood and clay will wash away,
Wash away, wash away,
Wood and clay will wash away,
My fair lady.

Build it up with bricks and mortar,
Bricks and mortar, bricks and mortar.
Build it up with bricks and mortar,
My fair lady.

Bricks and mortar will not stay,
Will not stay, will not stay.
Bricks and mortar will not stay,
My fair lady.

The Big Ship Sails on the Ally-Ally-Oh

The big ship sails on the ally-ally-oh,
The ally-ally-oh, the ally-ally-oh.
Oh, the big ship sails on the ally-ally-oh
On the last day of September.

The captain said, it will never, never do,
Never, never do, never, never do.
The captain said, it will never, never do,
On the last day of September.

The big ship sank to the bottom of the sea,
The bottom of the sea, the bottom of the sea.
The big ship sank to the bottom of the sea,
On the last day of September.

We all dip our heads in the deep blue sea,
The deep blue sea, the deep blue sea.
We all dip our heads in the deep blue sea,
On the last day of September.

Sally Go Round the Sun

Sally go round the sun. Sally go round the moon. Sally go round the chimney pots, on a Saturday afternoon.

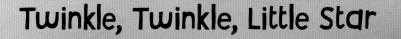

Twinkle, Twinkle, Little Star

Twinkle, twinkle, little star,
How I wonder what you are!
Up above the world so high,
Like a diamond in the sky.
Twinkle, twinkle, little star,
How I wonder what you are!

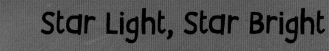

Star Light, Star Bright

Star light, star bright,
First star I see tonight,
I wish I may,
I wish I might,
Have the wish I wish tonight.

Hush, Little Baby

Hush, little baby, don't say a word.
Papa's gonna buy you a mockingbird.
And if that mockingbird won't sing,
Papa's gonna buy you a diamond ring.

And if that diamond ring turns brass,
Papa's gonna buy you a looking glass.
And if that looking glass gets broke,
Papa's gonna buy you a billy goat.

And if that billy goat won't pull,
Papa's gonna buy you a cart and bull.
And if that cart and bull turn over,
Papa's gonna buy you a dog called Rover.

And if that dog named Rover won't bark,
Papa's gonna buy you a horse and cart.
And if that horse and cart fall down,
You'll still be the sweetest little baby in town.

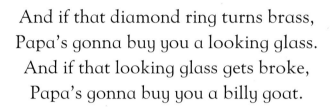

Sleep, Baby, Sleep

Sleep, baby, sleep,
Your father guards the sheep;
Your mother shakes the dreamland tree,
And from it fall sweet dreams for thee.
Sleep, baby, sleep.

Bye, Baby Bunting

Bye, Baby Bunting,
Daddy's gone a-hunting,
Gone to get a rabbit skin
To wrap the baby Bunting in.

Teddy Bear, Teddy Bear

Teddy Bear, Teddy Bear,
Go upstairs.
Teddy Bear, Teddy Bear,
Say your prayers.

Teddy Bear, Teddy Bear,
Turn out the light.
Teddy Bear, Teddy Bear,
Say good night.

Golden Slumbers

Golden slumbers kiss your eyes,
Smiles awake you when you rise;
Sleep, pretty baby, do not cry,
And I will sing you a lullaby.
Thomas Dekker

Skye Boat Song

Speed, bonnie boat, like a bird on the wing,
Onward! the sailors cry,
Carry the lad that's born to be King,
Over the sea to Skye.

Other books by Kali Stileman:

★ Big Book of My World ★ Big Book of Nursery Rhymes
★ My Book of Favourite Rhymes ★ My Book of First Words
★ My Book of Numbers, Shapes and Colours
★ Peely Wally ★ Time for Tea, Polly Wally

MY BOOK OF SONGS AND LULLABIES
A PICTURE CORGI BOOK 978 0 552 56401 4

First published in Great Britain as part of BIG BOOK OF NURSERY RHYMES by Doubleday in 2012,
an imprint of Random House Children's Publishers UK A Random House Group Company

This Picture Corgi edition published 2013

1 3 5 7 9 10 8 6 4 2

Picture Corgi Books are published by Random House Children's Publishers UK,
61–63 Uxbridge Road, London W5 5SA

www.randomhousechildrens.co.uk
www.randomhouse.co.uk

Addresses for companies within The Random House Group Limited can be found at:
www.randomhouse.co.uk/offices.htm

THE RANDOM HOUSE GROUP Limited Reg. No. 954009

A CIP catalogue record for this book is available from the British Library.

Printed in China